IF YOU WERE THERE

VIKING TIMES

Written by
Antony Mason

MARSHALL PUBLISHING • LONDON

CONTENTS

INTRODUCTION

"Deliver us, O Lord, from the fury of the Norsemen." With these words terrified people throughout northern Europe, in about A.D. 800, prayed urgently to God. By Norsemen they meant the Vikings – people from the North. The Vikings arrived stealthily in sleek ships and raided and plundered. They terrorised the coasts of England and the rest of Europe. They are remembered in history as ruthless, dangerous pirates.

But this history was written mainly by Christian monks – who were frequent victims of Viking raids. In fact there was much more to the Vikings than this. They had their own culture, gods and colourful myths. They were skilled shipbuilders, courageous explorers, enterprising traders and hardy settlers. They later settled peaceably in various parts of Europe, Iceland, Greenland and even North America.

Today we have plenty of evidence of Viking civilisation. Yet all this is still not quite enough to wipe away the Vikings' reputation as raiders – and the memories of the terror they struck throughout Europe for the 300 years when they ruled the seas.

VIKING RAIDS

In A.D. 793 the Vikings launched a surprise attack on the monastery of Lindisfarne, England. This was the first recorded Viking raid. They stole valuable treasures from the monastery, and killed any monks who got in their way. Then they loaded the stolen goods onto their ships and sailed home to Scandinavia (Norway, Sweden and Denmark).

The following summer they were back; killing, stealing and taking home prisoners to work as slaves. Within a few years these savage warriors were terrorising all the coasts of western Europe. Their fast, light ships also allowed them to travel up rivers to raid inland.

A round tower in Ireland

In Ireland monks built tall "round towers", which had very thick stone walls. When the Vikings attacked, the monks climbed up to the high entrance on a ladder which they then pulled up and locked themselves in. Safe inside, the monks waited until the Vikings went away.

Berserkrs were wild warriors who worked themselves up into a frenzy before a battle. They fought naked or wore animal skins. *Berserkr* meant "bear shirt", but it is the origin of our expression "going berserk".

Viking helmets

The Vikings wore strong iron helmets. Most were simple cup shapes, with a tongue of metal to protect the nose. Some were more elaborate, with a spectacle-shaped mask to protect the eyes and nose, and flaps to protect the neck. Despite the popular image of Vikings, their helmets did not have horns: it would have been too easy for an enemy to grab these, or to strike them with a fatal sword blow.

A wealthy Viking chieftain could afford to protect his body with a tunic of chain mail, made of thousands of iron rings. Most warriors were protected by padded leather jerkins (tunics).

A selection of Viking helmets

Stolen treasure

By the time the Vikings were raiding Europe, Christian monasteries had become centres of culture and learning. They were also very rich and powerful, and owned large areas of land and some of the greatest treasures in Europe. To the Vikings, who were not Christian, the monasteries were just an easy source of rich plunder. They stole any valuable treasures that they could carry away with them, such as the Scottish casket pictured above.

The Vikings almost always fought on foot; they very rarely used horses in battle.

Each raiding ship carried about 35 warriors and crew.

WEAPONS

Spear

A Viking warrior's most important weapon was his sword. It usually had two edges of pin-sharp steel, for stabbing and slashing. He defended himself with a wooden shield. Other weapons included spears and large battle-axes. Bows and arrows were sometimes used.

Iron sword

Iron axe, with silver decorations

Wooden shield, with an iron stud in the centre

Bow and arrows

◀*Many monasteries were built near the coast, or on a river. The Vikings brought their ships close to the target of their raid. Then they leapt out and attacked with such ferocity that few people could resist them. The Vikings attacked northern Europe over 300 years after the Romans had left. The armies of Europe were not well organised enough to defend their lands against them.*

VIKING RAIDS

ICELAND
NORWAY
SWEDEN
FINLAND
Volga
DENMARK
Baltic Sea
Dnieper
Kiev
SCOTLAND
IRELAND
ENGLAND
York
Dublin
London
Hamburg
Dorestad
Cologne
Danube
Black Sea
Rouen
Paris
Constantinople
Arles
Luna
ITALY
SPAIN
Mediterranean Sea
Seville Cordoba
Cadiz

Raid route from Sweden
Raid route from Norway
Raid route from Denmark

▲*The Vikings' raids gradually took them around the coasts of Europe. By about A.D. 860, they had reached the Mediterranean Sea and the coast of Italy. The Swedish Vikings travelled down the Dnieper and Volga rivers to reach the Mediterranean and Black seas.*

7

THE VIKING HOMELANDS

A gold ring

Back home in Scandinavia, the Vikings lived in small communities of farmers and traders. Most Vikings were farmers. They grew crops, raised farm animals and fished and hunted.

The landscape of Scandinavia is varied. Norway is mountainous; Sweden is flatter, with farmland and forests; Denmark is dotted with hundreds of small islands. Today each of these countries speaks its own language, but the Vikings probably all spoke versions of Old Norse.

Life in these regions was especially hard during the long, cold winters. The farmers had to make sure they had enough food stored away to last them through to the spring. If the crops failed, starvation threatened.

▼ *Most Vikings lived in small villages, sharing large, barnlike houses, called "halls" or "longhouses", with members of their immediate family, as well as other relatives. In winter the animals were kept indoors, either in separate sheds or in the halls themselves. The Vikings were well prepared for winter: they had sledges, skates, skis and shoes with studs in the soles to prevent them from slipping on the ice.*

◄ *The coast of Norway is pitted with hundreds of deep bays called fjords, created by glaciers millions of years ago. The good farm land – if there is any at all – lies on the shores of the fjords. It is often just a narrow strip between the water and the steep mountains.*

Winter cloaks were worn by men and women. At night they could be used as blankets.

Farm produce

The Vikings' most important crop was grain, which was used to make bread and porridge. Farmers grew barley, oats and rye. Wheat was considered a luxury and only the rich could afford it. Wild nuts and berries were also collected. The Vikings did not have potatoes or tomatoes. Food became scarce in the winter, but some of the vegetables they grew could be stored.

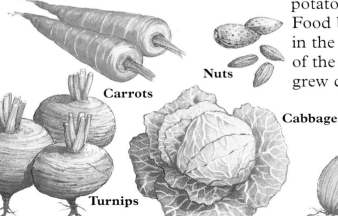

Carrots

Nuts

Cabbage

Onions

Turnips

Farm animals

The Vikings reared farm animals for meat, milk, eggs, wool and leather. Farm animals were very valuable and Viking farmers used every part of them. Even the feathers of chickens and geese were kept to make warm quilts. A large number of animals were slaughtered before the winter began, because otherwise they would eat valuable stored food. The meat was preserved by salting or smoking.

Longhorn cow

Goat

Sheep

Pig

Geese

Chickens

The chimney was just a hole in the roof. The inside of Viking homes smelled strongly of wood smoke and animals. There were usually no windows – or perhaps just one window, closed by shutters in winter.

Winter clothes were made of thick woollen cloth. Summer clothes were made of lighter wool, or linen, which was woven from flax plants.

Men wore a tunic called a *kyrtil*, with a belt around the middle.

Animal bones were used to make the blades of skates.

SOCIAL STRUCTURE

There were three main classes of Vikings: the jarls, *the* karls, *and the* thralls. *The* jarls *were the aristocracy. The* karls, *the largest group, included the farmers, traders and craftsmen. The* thralls *were slaves (usually prisoners of war or criminals). They could earn or buy their freedom and become* karls. *If a Viking fell on hard times he could sell himself into thralldom and buy his way out later.*

Jarl (chieftain or nobleman)

Thrall (slave)

Karls (free man and woman)

At Home with the Family

A quern stone for grinding grain

The Vikings lived very close to one another – eating, sleeping, working and playing under one roof. Their homes were very simple inside, usually consisting of one large, dingy room with an earth floor. Children did not go to school, but they had to help out on the farm and in the home from an early age. They learned skills from their parents or other adults. Some children, especially boys, were sent away for a year or so on travels, or to live with foster parents, as part of their education.

Living so closely with others meant that sometimes bitter arguments developed between families – perhaps over an insult or an act of treachery or a murder. These arguments might turn into long feuds between families that could last for several generations.

Viking women

Women were at the centre of Viking life. The men were often away for long periods of time on raiding or trading trips, so the women had to run the home. They raised their children, tended to domestic chores and looked after the farms. A wife conducted family business affairs when her husband was away. As a symbol of her position, a wealthy wife would wear a brooch with her keys, and perhaps her purse, dangling from it.

A woman's brooch

▼*In the middle of every hall was the hearth – a low fireplace. This was where the cooking was done, but it also provided warmth in winter. The fire was kept lit all the time, and at night it was the main source of light. There was very little furniture in a hall. There might be a table, a few stools and chests. But most people sat around the edge of the hall on the broad benches that doubled as beds.*

Farm animals were brought into the hall in winter. They were kept in stalls at one end.

Most food was cooked by boiling it in pots, grilling it over the open fire or baking it on hot stones. The most common foods were porridge made of oats or barley, and barley bread.

Entertainment

The Vikings liked to play a variety of games in their time off, or to while away the dark, cold days of winter. Board games included *hneftafl* – a form of draughts. In summer they played vigorous outdoor ball games, and challenged each other to wrestling and swimming matches, which involved fighting as well as swimming. These rough sports were considered a good way of training warriors.

Hneftafl

Many of the kitchen utensils were made of wood. The Vikings usually ate off wooden boards, using knives and spoons and their fingers.

Large brooches were used to attach the shoulder straps to the top of the dress.

Possessions – such as tools, weapons and food – were kept on hooks and shelves on the walls. Clothes were usually stored in chests.

Pieces from a board game

Bone flute

▲ *The most common musical instruments were simple wind instruments, such as flutes or panpipes. The Vikings also played a form of harp.*

VIKING SAGAS

The Vikings liked to be entertained by a skald, a performing storyteller and poet, who recounted tales of great adventures and warriors, mythical heroes of the past and the deeds (and misdeeds) of the gods. The tales were called sagas, and they were passed down through generations of families for hundreds of years before they were ever written down. Skalds were particularly in demand for feasts and at the courts of chieftains. The sagas also provided a kind of education as they represented a great storehouse of knowledge about Viking history, religion, laws and customs.

A skald

SHIPS

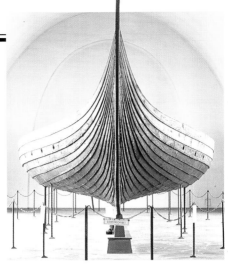

The Vikings' ancestors had a long history of trading. For hundreds of years they had crossed the seas to do business with the ports of northern Europe; they became wealthy by trading within the Roman empire. This trade continued during the A.D. 500s and A.D. 600s when Scandinavia had a "Golden Age".

During the A.D. 700s, the population of Scandinavia grew – and soon there was not enough good land to feed and house everyone. It was at this time that the Vikings began their raids to win loot, and also to find new lands in which to settle their families.

In order to travel to raid and settle, the Vikings needed good boats. They became the best shipbuilders in Europe, developing a fast, sleek kind of vessel for their warriors, the longship, with which they ruled the sea for 300 years.

A wooden dragon's head, found with the Oseberg ship

▲ *We have a good knowledge of what Viking ships looked like because a few have survived in burial mounds. Chieftains and other nobles were often buried in ships. A noble woman was buried in the Oseberg ship (above), which dates to the A.D. 800s. It was dug up in 1904 and rebuilt, and it now stands in a museum in Oslo, Norway.*

Navigation

When sailing far out to sea, out of sight of land, the Vikings found their way by studying the position of the sun, stars and planets, by watching the flight of seabirds heading for land, and by the feel of the currents and swell of the ocean. It is possible that, in later years, they used a bearing dial, an instrument which can show a bearing (compass direction) from the shadow of the sun.

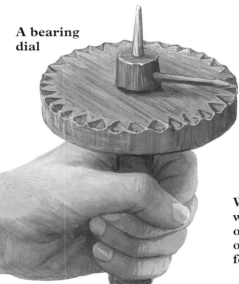

A bearing dial

The rudder was like a paddle fixed to the right-hand part of the ship, near the stern. This "steering board" was the origin of our term "starboard" (the right side of the ship).

Wooden planks were later laid over the bottom of the ship to form a deck.

▼ *Longships were built on a framework rising from an oak keel. Overlapping oak planks were pinned to this frame to form the sides. U-shaped ribs were then fixed to the planks. These raiding ships floated high in the water – so they could travel up shallow rivers. They could be powered by sail and by oars. The Viking warriors on board were extremely fit: they had to be able to fight after the exhausting work of rowing for hours on end.*

The ship's bow and stern (front and back) looked very much alike, but the bow was usually decorated with a carved figurehead, often in the shape of a dragon. This gave rise to the longships' other name: "dragon ships".

The planks were fixed with iron nails.

The overlapping planks were sealed, or "caulked", with a mixture of animal hairs and tar made from pine wood.

Trading ships

For trade, the Vikings used a different kind of ship, called a *knorr*. It was wider, heavier and slower than a longship, but its broad shape was designed to carry plenty of cargo, including live animals. *Knorrs* were usually powered by sails, but could also be rowed by oars from positions toward the bow and stern. They could carry up to 40 passengers on long journeys, and they were used for the Vikings' voyages of exploration to distant lands. All ships had open decks; if it rained, the Vikings sheltered under animal skins.

SHIPBUILDING TOOLS

To shape their timber and to carve the figurehead at the bow, the Viking shipbuilders had a limited set of simple tools made of iron and wood. Raw timber was shaped into beams and planks using axes and adzes, a type of cutting tool. Moulding irons were used to carve grooves along the line of the planks.

Hacksaw

Moulding iron

Auger or drill

Wood saw

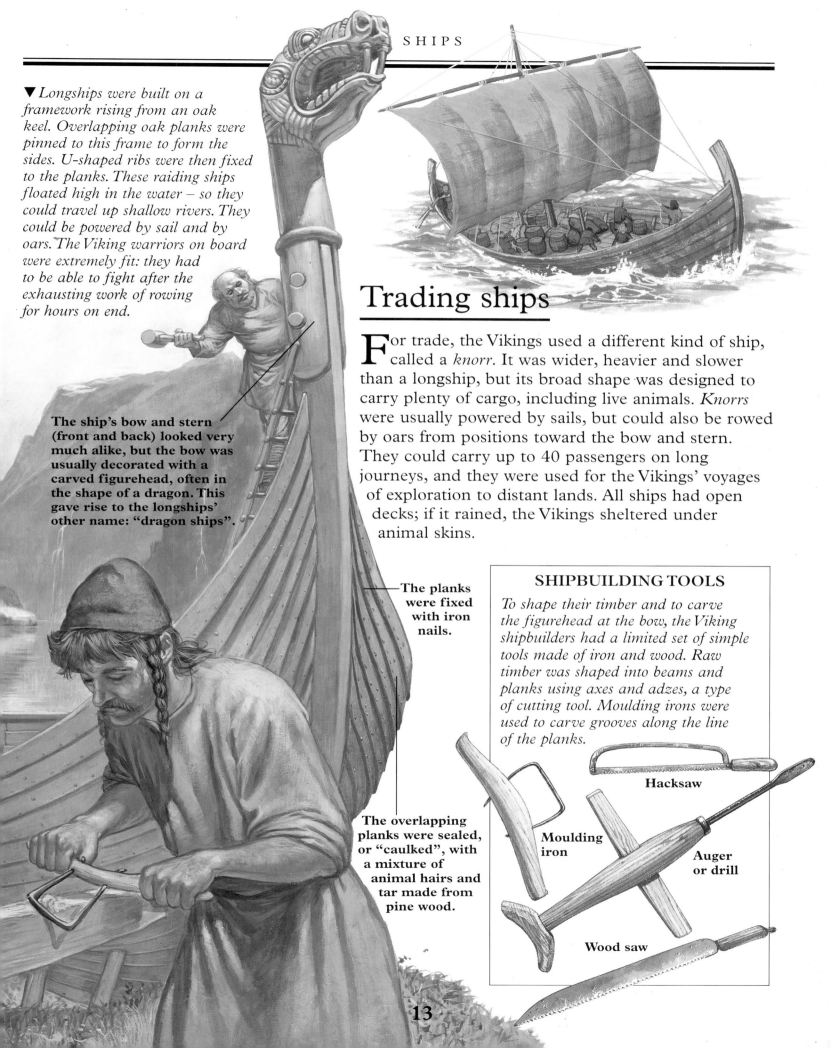

EXPLORERS AND SETTLERS

A house in Iceland roofed with turf

The Vikings did not only raid; they also went in search of lands to settle. The first foreign Viking settlements were winter bases, used between their summer raids.

In A.D. 865 the Danes invaded England with a huge fleet. They took over much of the north and east of England. Within 15 years they had settled this region, which became known as the Danelaw. Only Wessex in southern England, ruled by Alfred the Great (A.D. 871–899), was not taken by them. Later, the English paid the Vikings "Danegeld" (a bribe) to stop them from raiding.

Meanwhile, Swedes known as Rus moved into Central Europe to land occupied by the Slavs, and were invited to rule. They took over Kiev, creating the most important "Russian" state, the Kingdom of Kiev.

Iceland and Greenland

The Vikings also ventured into the North Atlantic. They explored and settled in Iceland after A.D. 860. From here Erik the Red sailed to Greenland in about A.D. 986. He managed to persuade settlers to join him by calling this icy land "green". Some 3,000 Vikings lived in Greenland, and their settlements survived there for about 400 years.

▼ *The Vikings took over ports and other settlements and developed them in the style of their towns back in Scandinavia. The houses were smaller than their own village longhouses, and were packed closely together along narrow streets.*

Where timber was plentiful the Vikings built houses of wood. The roof might be made of planks, covered with straw thatch secured by leather thongs.

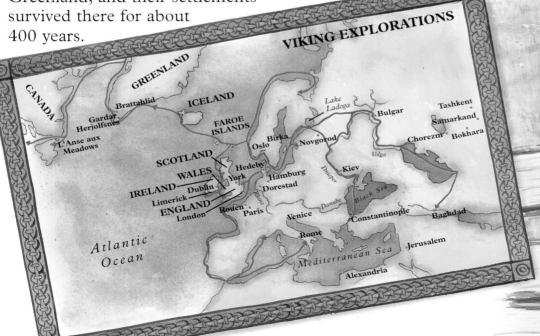

VIKING EXPLORATIONS

CANADA
GREENLAND
Brattahlid
Gardar
Herjolfsnes
L'Anse aux Meadows
ICELAND
FAROE ISLANDS
SCOTLAND
WALES
IRELAND
Limerick
Dublin
ENGLAND
London
York
Hedeby
Hamburg
Dorestad
Rouen
Paris
Oslo
Birka
Novgorod
Lake Ladoga
Bulgar
Kiev
Volga
Dnieper
Rhine
Danube
Venice
Rome
Black Sea
Constantinople
Tashkent
Samarkand
Chorezm
Bokhara
Baghdad
Jerusalem
Mediterranean Sea
Alexandria
Atlantic Ocean

▼ *In new settlements, the houses were built with whatever materials were available. The Vikings were used to building with wood, but in Greenland and parts of Iceland there was very little wood so they made houses using stone and turf.*

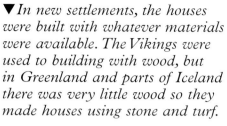

Walls made of wooden planks

Walls made of a wooden frame filled with clay

Walls made of tree trunks

Walls and roof made of turf on a stone foundation

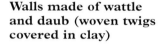

Walls made of wattle and daub (woven twigs covered in clay)

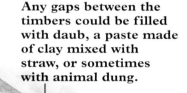

Any gaps between the timbers could be filled with daub, a paste made of clay mixed with straw, or sometimes with animal dung.

The Vikings in America

In about A.D. 1000 Leif Eriksson, the son of Erik the Red, sailed westward from Greenland until he came to lands which he named Helluland, Markland and Vinland. They were probably Baffin Island, Labrador and Newfoundland, now parts of Canada. This means that the Vikings reached the Americas about 500 years before Columbus. They tried to settle on these coasts but left after being attacked by North American Indians, whom they called Skraelings ("wretches"). In 1968 the remains of a Viking settlement were found at L'Anse aux Meadows in Newfoundland.

A Skraeling

THE ALTHING

In Viking society, all freemen could attend a kind of open-air meeting called the Thing, which took place every two years or so. Here they could discuss the problems that faced the community. It was an early form of democratic government. In Iceland a national parliament called the Althing met outdoors at Thingvellir for two weeks every summer. Today the Icelandic parliament in Reykjavik is still called the Althing.

MERCHANTS AND TRADERS

A silver penny minted in York

Many of the Viking settlements were also trading bases. Several towns in Scandinavia became major trading centres, notably Birka (Sweden) and Hedeby (Denmark). Gradually the Vikings created a trading network that spread far and wide across Europe. The Swedish Vikings traded around the Baltic Sea, and also followed the rivers across eastern Europe to the Caspian and Black seas.

The Kingdom of Kiev lay on these important trade routes, linking Asia with northern Europe. By the 11th century, the Rus Vikings ruled all the land that stretched between the Black Sea and the Baltic Sea.

Once they had taken control of the Slav lands and much of eastern Europe, the Rus traders no longer needed to be heavily armed. Instead of helmets, they wore fur hats.

◄ *Rouen, (the modern city and port pictured here) on the River Seine in northern France, was attacked repeatedly by the Vikings after A.D. 841. In A.D. 911 the region was handed over to Viking settlers. Rouen developed as a major port and trading centre, and became the capital of Viking Normandy.*

Weights and measures

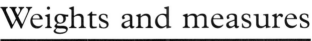

The Vikings usually traded by barter, a method of swapping one item or service for another, such as timber for a valuable fur. But they also used coins. As well as minting their own coins, they traded in silver Arab coins, many thousands of which have been found in Sweden; some even reached Scotland. Generally, the Vikings used coins as a source of precious metal. Merchants would weigh the coins on a pair of scales, using a reliable set of weights, to determine their value.

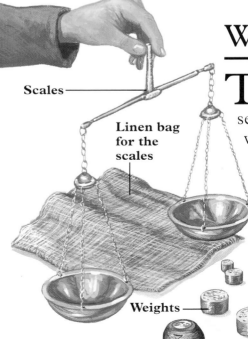

Scales

Linen bag for the scales

Weights

The religion of Islam reached the shores of the Caspian and Black seas during the A.D. 600s and A.D. 700s. Viking traders would have seen Muslim mosques like this.——

▼Viking traders came into contact with the Arabs around the Black and Caspian seas, where they bargained for exotic goods from the East. Some even travelled as far as Baghdad. Many of these traders were Vikings from the Rus territories, such as the Kingdom of Kiev.

The Arab World was connected to the ancient Silk Road that ran across Asia to China. The Vikings were able to buy Chinese silk cloth from Arab merchants.

Portage

There are no rivers that flow all the way from the Baltic Sea to the Black Sea, or the Caspian Sea. Therefore, to reach these destinations, the Vikings had to take their goods up one river and down another. They had to transport their goods – and occasionally their boats – between the rivers. This was known as "portage". To travel by boat between Novgorod and Constantinople, for instance, the Viking traders had to take their boats overland between the Dnieper and Lovat rivers.

TRADE GOODS

The Vikings sold ordinary things such as food, farm animals, leather and timber, as well as more valuable commodities – for instance, walrus ivory and amber (fossilised tree sap) that were used to make jewellery. In return, they bought wine, silks, spices, precious jewellery and silver coins.

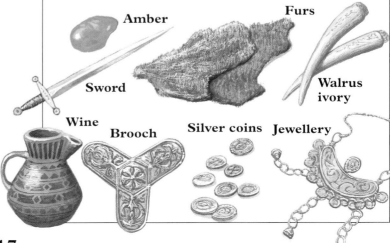

Amber

Furs

Sword

Walrus ivory

Wine

Brooch

Silver coins

Jewellery

17

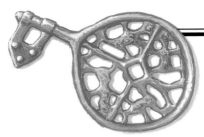

A bronze key

ARTS AND CRAFTS

Traders brought jewellery, glassware and Persian leatherwork to the Viking settlements of Scandinavia and northern Europe. But the Vikings themselves were also highly skilled artists and craftworkers.

Smiths were important figures in Viking communities. They made iron farm tools, kitchen implements, locks and keys and weapons. They also made beautiful brooches and cloak pins out of bronze, silver and gold.

The Vikings were skilled stoneworkers and woodcarvers and adorned their ships, furniture and buildings with delicately sculpted patterns.

Hundreds of Viking treasures and other more ordinary objects have been found – many of them preserved in graves. The treasures tell us about the Vikings' sense of beauty; the ordinary objects tell us how they lived.

▼ *Wood played an important part in Viking life – it was used to make ships, houses, furniture, tools, chests, buckets and barrels. Professional carpenters usually worked in towns and villages and made whatever their customers ordered. They mainly used hand-held tools, and occasionally a lathe to shape round objects.*

Children learned a trade from an early age by working alongside their parents.

All handmade

The Vikings had to make virtually everything themselves – including all the equipment and implements they needed in the home. Most ordinary objects were made of wood, leather, iron and clay. Bone was used to make needles and handles. Deer antlers were used to make combs. Pots were often carved out of soapstone, a soft stone found in Norway.

Clay pot

Drainer for making cheese

Wooden bucket

Drinking cup

Iron knife

RUNES

The Vikings used a system of writing made up of letters called runes. The original alphabet (called futhark *after the first six letters) had 24 characters, but this later developed into 16 letters, pictured here with their equivalent sounds in our modern alphabet.*

F   U TH

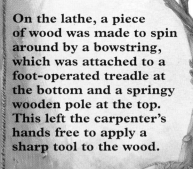

On the lathe, a piece of wood was made to spin around by a bowstring, which was attached to a foot-operated treadle at the bottom and a springy wooden pole at the top. This left the carpenter's hands free to apply a sharp tool to the wood.

Viking glass

Throughout Viking times, glass was a luxury, imported at great expense from Germany and Italy. Viking glassmakers melted down pieces of glass to make colourful beads. Later they learned how to create more complex shapes, such as drinking vessels shaped like their traditional cups which were made of animal horns.

Glass drinking horn

Weaving and clothes

Most of the Vikings' clothes were made from woollen or linen cloth which was woven on upright looms by the women. They used natural dyes made of plants and minerals to produce a range of soft colours. The cloth could be woven with yarns of the various colours to produce stripes; or the clothes themselves could be decorated with richly embroidered patterns, or with bands of bright ribbons.

Woman's underdress

Child's trousers

Woman's headscarf

Stone carved with the original rune alphabet

Man's woollen tunic

Woman's linen headdress

R K H N I A S T B M L R

19

VIKING GODS

A statue of Odin

The Vikings believed in many gods and goddesses, and they told stories about them and their magical world of monsters and evil giants. These stories helped the Vikings to explain the mysteries of the world around them – such as the changing seasons and crop failures.

We know very little about how the Vikings worshipped their gods. It seems that they did not usually have temples or priests, but that they made offerings and said prayers to please a specific god who might help them. They celebrated three major annual festivals, at which sacrifices to the gods took place: *Sigrblot* (early summer), *Vetrarblot* (early autumn) and *Jolablot* (mid-winter).

Loki the trickster

Not all the Viking gods were good. Loki was a trickster who took on all kinds of cunning disguises. He was dishonest and unreliable, but the gods and giants knew that he would happily help them with any trickery they planned. Loki was the father of three monsters: Fenrir the giant wolf, Jormungand the serpent and Hel, who was half woman, half skeleton, and became Queen of the Dead.

King of the gods

The chief god was Odin. He ruled over Asgard, the kingdom of the gods. Odin was the god of battle, victory, courage and poetry. He rode an eight-legged horse and he caused wars by throwing down his magical spear. He had two ravens called Thought and Memory, which flew around the world and informed him about all they had seen. Odin's wife was Frigg, goddess of health, marriage and children.

At a feast, the food was washed down with large quantities of barley ale, mead (an alcoholic drink made of honey) and imported wine.

Skalds (storytellers) and other entertainers were hired to amuse the guests.

Guests wore their best clothes to a feast.

20

▼ *The stories about their gods contain many details from the Vikings' own lives. The idea of Valhalla reflects the Vikings' love of feasting. Feasts that would last for several days, or even weeks, were held at all great events – such as religious festivals, marriages and funerals.*

It was the women's job to ensure that there was enough food and drink at the feast.

Going to Valhalla

Viking warriors believed that if they died in battle their souls would be swept off the battlefield by winged female warriors, called Valkyries, and taken to Valhalla (the "Hall of the Slain Warriors"). This was Odin's great hall in his kingdom of Asgard. At Valhalla the dead warriors trained for *Ragnarök*, the last great battle between the gods and the evil monsters, after which a new, harmonious world would begin. This carved stone (left) from Gotland, Sweden, shows warriors travelling to Valhalla in a longship (bottom), and being welcomed by a Valkyrie (top).

Thor's Hammer

Many Vikings wore an amulet (lucky charm, right) representing *Miollnir*, the hammer of the god Thor. Thor, one of Odin's sons, was famous for his huge appetite for eating and drinking at feasts, and for using his magical hammer to defeat giants. People believed that *Miollnir* charms would protect them from evil. Thunder was said to be the sound of the wheels of Thor's chariot, which was drawn across the sky by giant goats. *Miollnir* means "lightning".

OTHER GODS

The Viking gods and goddesses belonged to two families, the Aesir and the Vanir. Farmers tended to worship the Vanir; warriors worshipped the Aesir. Odin and his family were Aesir. The most popular of the Vanir was Freyr, the god of fertility and peace. He controlled the rain and sunshine that made the crops grow. His twin sister, called Freyia, was the goddess of love and beauty, and was thought to have the gift of telling the future.

Statue of Freyr

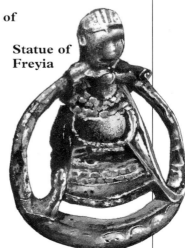

Statue of Freyia

BURYING THE DEAD

A pot filled with burned human bones and shield studs

The Vikings believed that the souls of people lived on after death. Good people went to join the gods in Asgard, and warriors went to Valhalla. Others would go to Niflheim, the icy Land of the Dead.

Dead people would need possessions in their afterlife. That is why food, weapons, tools, jewellery and many other things were put in the grave. Some people thought that the dead needed a ship to reach Asgard, so many rich chieftains and their wives were buried in ships.

Most people were buried in cemeteries close to their villages. Others were cremated (burned), along with their possessions, and their ashes were buried in a pot.

▼ *Wealthy Vikings had dramatic funerals. The body and all the grave goods were placed on a ship, and then burned or buried. An Arab merchant called Ibn Fadlan saw one of these funerals in A.D. 921, on the Volga River. He wrote a detailed account of this Viking cremation.*

The closest relatives of the dead person set fire to the funeral pyre (wood pile) with a flaming torch.

Funerals were treated as major events, attended by large crowds and accompanied by feasting.

The Oseberg Ship

In 1903 a buried Viking ship was discovered at Oseberg in Norway. It was the tomb of a noble woman, who had been buried with her maid or slave in A.D. 834. The ship had been preserved under a mound of peat and stones. When it was dug up by archaeologists (pictured above), they found all kinds of things that had been buried with the dead woman, including furniture, sledges, cloth, shoes, buckets of food, and the remains of several horses. However, grave robbers had stolen all the jewellery and treasures. The ship was reconstructed even though stones in the mound had crushed it into 3,000 pieces (see page 12).

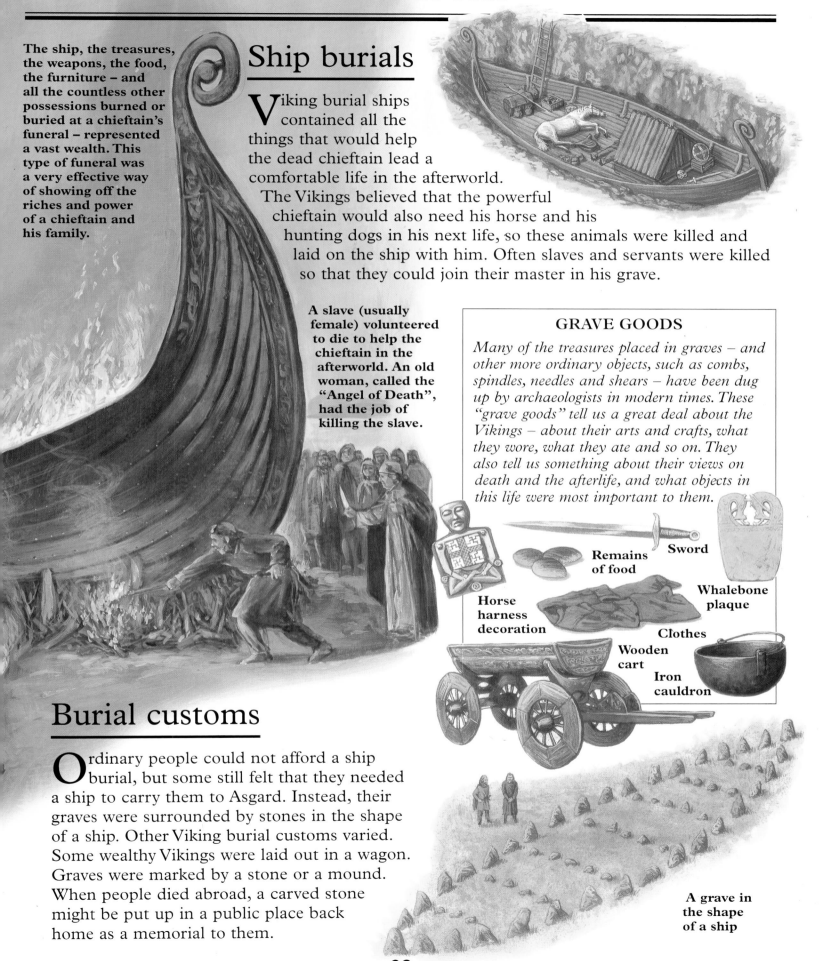

The ship, the treasures, the weapons, the food, the furniture – and all the countless other possessions burned or buried at a chieftain's funeral – represented a vast wealth. This type of funeral was a very effective way of showing off the riches and power of a chieftain and his family.

Ship burials

Viking burial ships contained all the things that would help the dead chieftain lead a comfortable life in the afterworld.

The Vikings believed that the powerful chieftain would also need his horse and his hunting dogs in his next life, so these animals were killed and laid on the ship with him. Often slaves and servants were killed so that they could join their master in his grave.

A slave (usually female) volunteered to die to help the chieftain in the afterworld. An old woman, called the "Angel of Death", had the job of killing the slave.

GRAVE GOODS

Many of the treasures placed in graves – and other more ordinary objects, such as combs, spindles, needles and shears – have been dug up by archaeologists in modern times. These "grave goods" tell us a great deal about the Vikings – about their arts and crafts, what they wore, what they ate and so on. They also tell us something about their views on death and the afterlife, and what objects in this life were most important to them.

Remains of food

Sword

Whalebone plaque

Horse harness decoration

Clothes

Wooden cart

Iron cauldron

Burial customs

Ordinary people could not afford a ship burial, but some still felt that they needed a ship to carry them to Asgard. Instead, their graves were surrounded by stones in the shape of a ship. Other Viking burial customs varied. Some wealthy Vikings were laid out in a wagon. Graves were marked by a stone or a mound. When people died abroad, a carved stone might be put up in a public place back home as a memorial to them.

A grave in the shape of a ship

CHRISTIAN VIKINGS

An altar piece showing King Harald Bluetooth's baptism

The Vikings were exposed to Christianity from about the late ninth century onward. Gradually, they abandoned their own gods and adopted the Christian religion. The kings of the Scandinavian countries were among the first to accept Christianity in their homelands. King Harald Bluetooth of Denmark became a Christian in about A.D. 960. Olaf Tryggvason was a Christian when he became king of Norway in A.D. 995. King Olof Skötkonung of Sweden was baptised in A.D. 1008.

Once the Scandinavian kings had become Christians, their people followed. Some leaders used force to convert their subjects. Vladimir, prince of Kiev, became a Christian in A.D. 988, and then apparently herded all his people into the River Dnieper to be baptised. But usually Christianity spread slowly, and without force.

The Jelling Stone

A famous stone monument at Jelling in Denmark was set up by King Harald Bluetooth in memory of his parents, who may have been buried in one of the huge mounds close by. The stone is carved with a picture of Christ on the cross, and an inscription in runes states that Harald "made the Danes Christian". In fact this was an exaggeration: Denmark did not become fully Christian for another 100 years or more.

The Jelling stone

The upper rooftops were crowned with dragons, the same symbol that was used on the bows of the Viking longships. The roofs were covered in wooden tiles.

Christian crosses were placed on the lower rooftops.

The walls were made of planks or staves, giving rise to the name for this type of wooden church: a "stave church".

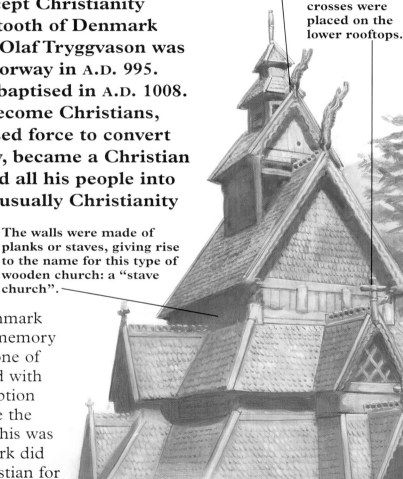

▶ *Some of the first churches in Scandinavia were built of wood. By the 11th century they had become tall, elaborate structures, like the one pictured here. This new design however, still reflected many of the old Viking traditions of building. Those churches that have survived are among the oldest wooden buildings in the world.*

24

Christian kings

During the Viking age, Norway, Sweden and Denmark developed as separate kingdoms, each with its own king. The kings were constantly fighting each other. After about A.D. 960 Christianity played an important part in these power struggles because alliances could be made with other Christian kings. To protect his Christian kingdom from invaders, King Harald Bluetooth built a series of impressive circular fortresses, such as this one at Trelleborg.

The Trelleborg fortress

Inside the church was a single, tall room. The woodwork was often heavily carved with interlacing patterns and pictures, in Viking style.

MIXED FAITHS

The Vikings often accepted Christianity publicly, but continued to worship the Viking gods in private. They were practical people – they realised that, when trading with Christians, it helped if they said that they were Christians too. Many Vikings followed both religions: they worshipped in a Christian church, but in times of danger (such as a storm at sea) they would call on Thor for help. A stone mould found in Denmark shows how a metalsmith could cast Thor's hammer and Christian crosses at the same time.

Cross **Thor's hammer** **Cross**

From king to saint

Stone carving of Saint Olaf

When Olaf Tryggvason became king of Norway in A.D. 995, he tried, but failed, to convert his own people to Christianity. In A.D. 1014, the Christian Olaf Haraldsson, took the throne. He used threats and violence to try to convert the Norwegians, but after attacking Denmark unsuccessfully in A.D. 1028, he had to flee to Russia. When he tried to reclaim his throne in A.D. 1030, he was killed in battle. He was buried as a Christian martyr in a shrine in Trondheim cathedral, and became the patron saint of Norway.

THE NORMANS

William the Conqueror

In A.D. 1066 England was attacked by invaders trying to claim the English throne. One such group was the Norwegian Vikings led by Harald Hardrada. The other invaders were the Normans – descendants of Norsemen (Vikings) who had settled in northern France in the 10th century.

The Normans were led by William, Duke of Normandy (William the Conqueror), who became King of England in A.D. 1066. He was a descendant of the Danish Viking leader, Rollo. In A.D. 911 Charles III, King of France, had given Rollo a small territory in northern France to stop him from invading the area. Rollo expanded this territory, and it developed into the powerful Duchy of Normandy ("the land of the Northmen").

▼ The Normans defeated the English at the Battle of Hastings in A.D. 1066. The English were exhausted having just defeated a Norwegian invasion led by King Harald Hardrada at the Battle of Stamford Bridge in northern England. Later the Normans had to fight off a series of invasions by the Danes and Norwegians. But after A.D. 1098 the Viking invasions of Britain ceased. The Viking age had come to a close.

THE NORMAN LANDS
CIRCA A.D. 1100

ENGLAND

NORMANDY

ITALY

APULIA

CALABRIA

SICILY

ANTIOCH

Mediterranean Sea

The Norman army included skilled archers who fired arrows with deadly accuracy. During the Battle of Hastings, one of these arrows apparently struck the English king, Harold Godwinson, in the eye and killed him.

Norman lands

By the 11th century the Normans had emerged as one of the most powerful peoples in Europe. Their leaders had married into royalty and aristocracy. Norman soldiers fought in Spain and in Italy, and after the A.D. 1040s they began to take control of areas of southern Italy and Sicily. During the First Crusade (A.D. 1096–99) against the Muslims in the Middle East, they also captured Antioch.

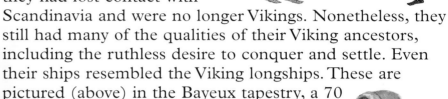

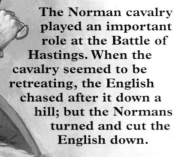

The Norman cavalry played an important role at the Battle of Hastings. When the cavalry seemed to be retreating, the English chased after it down a hill; but the Normans turned and cut the English down.

Like their Viking ancestors, the Normans wore chain mail and iron helmets with nose guards.

Invasion

By the time of the Norman Conquest of England, the Normans were French-speaking – they had lost contact with Scandinavia and were no longer Vikings. Nonetheless, they still had many of the qualities of their Viking ancestors, including the ruthless desire to conquer and settle. Even their ships resembled the Viking longships. These are pictured (above) in the Bayeux tapestry, a 70 metre-long work of embroidery that tells the story of the Norman invasion of England and the Battle of Hastings.

Varangian guard

In A.D. 988 Vladimir, prince of Kiev, sent Rus (or Varangian) warriors to Constantinople to act as personal bodyguards to Emperor Basil II. This "Varangian guard" protected the Byzantine emperors for over 100 years. One of their most famous commanders was Harald Hardrada ("the Ruthless"), who later became King of Norway (A.D. 1047–66).

THE NORMANS IN ITALY

A group of Normans led by Robert Guiscard and his brother Roger invaded southern Italy. By A.D. 1071 Robert had defeated the forces of the Byzantine empire and claimed the provinces of Apulia and Calabria. Roger took the island of Sicily from the Arabs in A.D. 1091. The rule of his Norman descendants in Sicily lasted until A.D. 1194. This was considered to be a "golden age", when many magnificent churches and palaces were built, mainly by Roger II (left), who was crowned king in A.D. 1130.

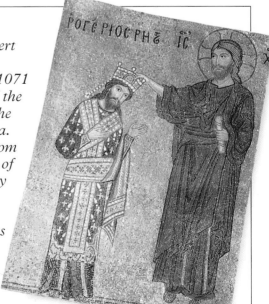

VIKING LANDS

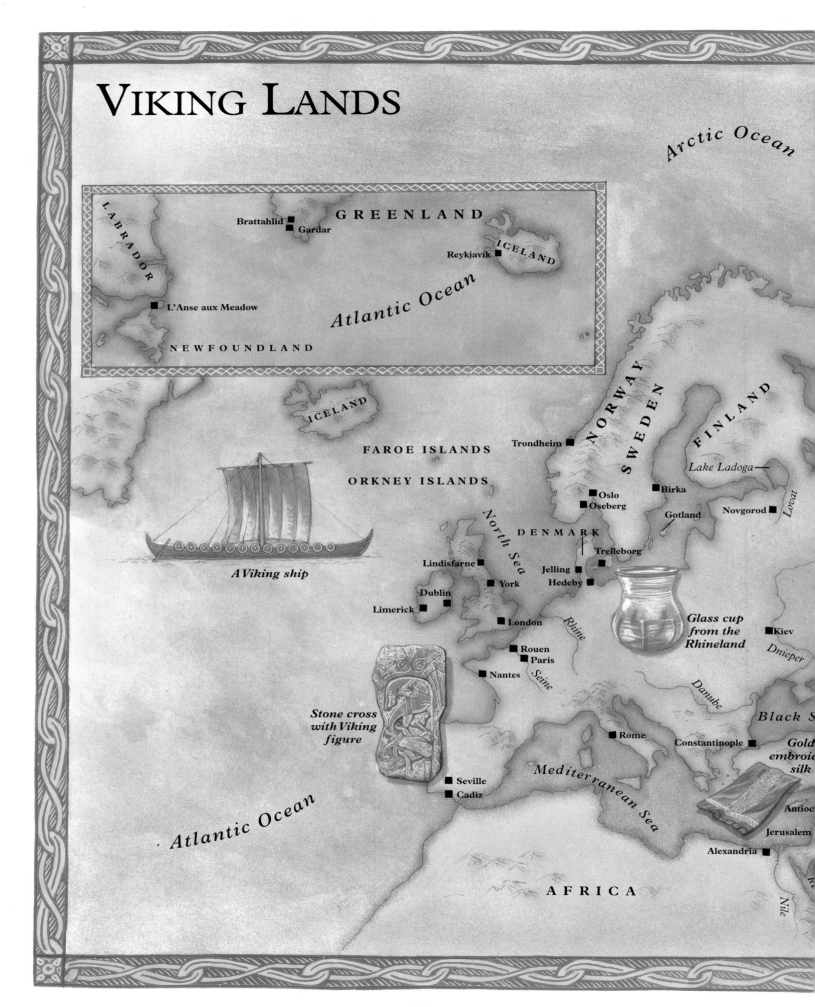

Arctic Ocean

LABRADOR

Brattahlid
Gardar

GREENLAND

ICELAND

Reykjavík

Atlantic Ocean

L'Anse aux Meadow

NEWFOUNDLAND

ICELAND

FAROE ISLANDS

ORKNEY ISLANDS

NORWAY

SWEDEN

FINLAND

Lake Ladoga

Trondheim

Birka

Oslo
Oseberg

Gotland

Novgorod

A Viking ship

North Sea

DENMARK

Trelleborg

Lindisfarne

Jelling

York

Hedeby

Dublin

Glass cup from the Rhineland

Kiev

Limerick

London

Rhine

Dnieper

Rouen
Paris

Nantes

Seine

Danube

Black Sea

Stone cross with Viking figure

Rome

Constantinople

Gold embroidered silk

Seville

Cadiz

Mediterranean Sea

Antioch

Jerusalem

Alexandria

Atlantic Ocean

AFRICA

Nile

INDEX

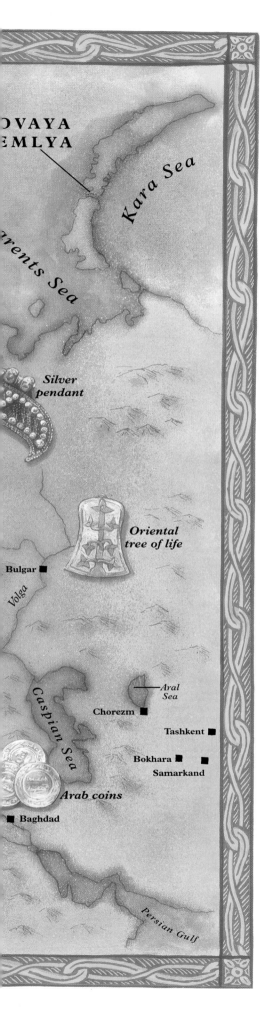

RAID, TRADE OR SETTLE

Ride your Viking ship on the high seas and face real Viking choices when you reach your destination. Do you raid, do you trade or do you settle? As either a Danish, Norwegian or Swedish Viking, race against the clock to gather as much treasure as possible before the Viking era ends!

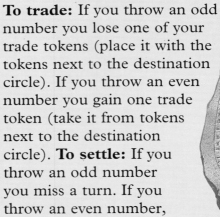

RULES

1. This is a game for two to three players. You will need the following: a die or spinner (pattern provided); coloured buttons for each player; 40 trading tokens; 3 life tokens for each player and a watch.

2. Each player starts on the "Home" circle, with three life tokens and four trade tokens. Place two trade tokens beside each of the destination circles on the map.

3. The aim is to collect trade tokens. The winner is the player with the most tokens when time expires.

4. This game lasts for 23 minutes exactly – that is 5 seconds for every year of the Viking era (A.D. 793–1066). Throw the die in turn and move along the path in any direction. Carry out the printed instructions when you land on them. When you reach a destination, you have a chance to win tokens – or to lose tokens or a life! Decide whether to raid, trade or settle and roll the die.

To raid: If you throw an odd number you lose a life. Place one of your life tokens in the box marked Valhalla. If you throw an even number you can take two trade tokens from that destination circle.

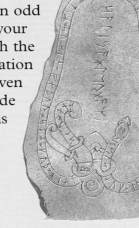

To trade: If you throw an odd number you lose one of your trade tokens (place it with the tokens next to the destination circle). If you throw an even number you gain one trade token (take it from tokens next to the destination circle). **To settle:** If you throw an odd number you miss a turn. If you throw an even number, take one token.

5. If you have to give up a trade token but have none left, you must give up a life token instead. If you lose all your life tokens you are out.

6. When 23 minutes are up, complete the round of play. Then count up all your trade tokens. The player with the most trade tokens wins. If two or all players have the same number of trade tokens, the one with the most life tokens left wins.

Copy the template on to a piece of thin cardboard. Cut it out and make a hole in the centre. Push a toothpick through the hole and your spinner is ready to use.